蔡志忠漫画中英文版

庄子说 ②

ZHUANG ZI SPEAKS II

自·然·的·箫·声

More Music of Nature

蔡志忠/著　BRIAN BRUYA(美)/译

现代出版社

Contents

The Giant Bird 3

Liezi Rides the Wind 4

Xu You Refuses the World 5

Who's the Master 6

Zhuangzi Speaks about Not
Speaking 7

Yao's Question 8

The Danger of Knowledge 9

The Man With One Leg 10

Qin Shi Didn't Cry 11

Mental Fasting 12

The Man on Fire 13

The Madman of Chu 14

Body and Spirit 15

Do People Have Emotions 16

What is a Genuine Person 17

The Dao is Higher than Heaven 18

Mindless of Each Other 19

Hiding the World in the World 20

Creation and Destruction 21

Yan Hui Sits in Forgetting 23

The Mind is Like a Mirror 25

The Death of Primal Chaos 26

The Sixth Finger 27

Great Confusion Alters One's
Nature 28

The Horse Trainer's Transgressions
29

The Harm of Benevolence and
Righteousness 31

Theft Prevention 32

The Lost Pearl 33

The Heavenly Dao 35

Governing Through Non-Action 36

Independent Liesure 37

Energy and Spirit 39

Recluses	40
Autumn Waters	41
Heaven and Earth and a Strand of Fur	43
Size and Limits	44
Status and the Dao	45
Alternating Functions	46
Fire Doesn't Burn	47
A Turtle in the Muck	48
Ultimate Joy	49
Zhuangzi Drums on a Pot	51
A Lump on the Elbow	53
People Neither Live Nor Die	54
Realm of the Perfect Person	55
Catching Cicadas	56
Steering a Boat	58
The Sacrificial Pigs	60
Swimming in a Waterfall	61
Qing Makes a Bell-Stand	62
Dongye Ji Has an Accident	63
Gong Chui's Fingers	64
Zhuangzi in the Brambles	65
Only One Confucian in Lu	66
Baili Xi Raises Oxen	68
The Genuine Painter	69
Perfect Archery	70
Self-Respect	72
Can the Dao Be Possessed	73
The Dao in Defecation	74
The Dao Transcends Knowledge	76
No Distractions	78
Breaking the Barriers	79
Ultimate Benevolence	80
Xu Wugui's Appraisals	81
The Exile	83
The King Kills a Special Monkey	85
The Realm of Ignorance	86
The Cyclic Dao	87
The Prince of Ren Goes Fishing	88
Confucius Changes	89
No Attachments	90
The Phases of Attaining the Dao	91
Life Is Most Important	92
The Goat Butcher Refuses Reward	93
Refusing Office	94
The Man Who Pursued Profit	95

Zhuangzi Speaks II
More Music of Nature

说剑、渔父、列御寇、天下。注者甚多，以唐郭象注本及清王先谦的庄子集解较佳。

乐、达生、山木、田子方、知北游；「杂篇」十一篇——庚桑楚、徐无鬼、则阳、外物、寓言、让王、盗跖、宗师、应帝王；「外篇」十五篇——骈拇、马蹄、胠箧、在宥、天地、天道、天运、刻意、缮性、秋水、至

现存为晋郭象所重编的三十三篇。即：「内篇」七篇——逍遥游、齐物论、养生主、人间世、德充符、大

庄子书，据汉志说有五十二篇，未受重视。至唐玄宗时代，始渐器重，被列入经书。

庄子名叫周，是宋国蒙地人。他曾做过蒙地漆园的官吏，跟梁惠王、齐宣王同时代。他的哲理，庄子的学问非常渊博，研究的范围无所不包，庄子之学，其要本归老子，可谓集道家之大成。

他的个性恬淡寡欲，不慕名利，楚威王闻知庄周贤能，遣使者带着重金币去聘请他，请他做卿相，却遭他婉辞拒绝。

对自然与人生有许多宝贵的启示。

Zhuangzi

The Giant Bird

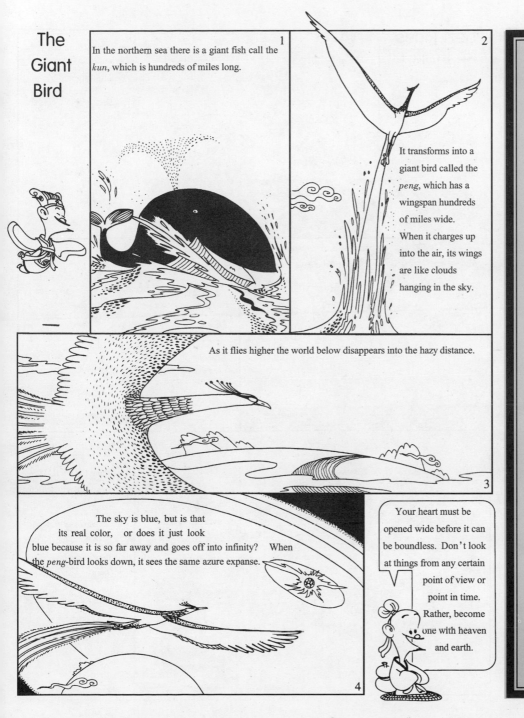

1 In the northern sea there is a giant fish call the *kun*, which is hundreds of miles long.

2 It transforms into a giant bird called the *peng*, which has a wingspan hundreds of miles wide. When it charges up into the air, its wings are like clouds hanging in the sky.

As it flies higher the world below disappears into the hazy distance. **3**

4 The sky is blue, but is that its real color, or does it just look blue because it is so far away and goes off into infinity? When the *peng*-bird looks down, it sees the same azure expanse.

Your heart must be opened wide before it can be boundless. Don't look at things from any certain point of view or point in time. Rather, become one with heaven and earth.

自然的箫声

庄子说

《庄子◎逍遥游第一》

已矣。

也。」野马也，尘埃也，生物之以息相吹也。天之苍苍，其正色邪？其远而无所至极邪？其视下也，亦若是则齐谐者，志怪者也。谐之言曰：「鹏之徙于南冥也，水击三千里，搏扶摇而上者九万里。去以六月息者飞，其翼若垂天之云。是鸟也，海运则将徙于南冥。南冥者，天池也。

北冥有鱼，其名为鲲。鲲之大，不知其几千里也；化而为鸟，其名为鹏。鹏之背，不知其几千里也；怒而

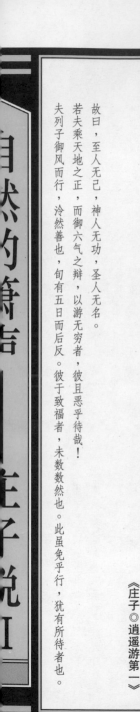

自然的箫声　庄子说 I

故曰，至人无己，神人无功，圣人无名。

若夫乘天地之正，而御六气之辩，以游无穷者，彼且恶乎待哉！

夫列子御风而行，泠然善也，旬有五日而后反。彼于致福者，未数数然也。此虽免乎行，犹有所待者也。

《庄子◎逍遥游第一》

Xu You Refuses the World

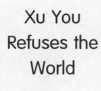

The legendary emperor Yao wished to resign as ruler and turn the land over to the hermit Xu You ...

I am like a torch vainly flickering in the brilliance of the sun or moon, which you resemble. I am like irrigation needlessly toiling, while the rains still come on time. Because you are much superior to me, please accept the world to rule.

1

Forget it! When a bird goes to nest in a tree, all it needs is a single branch.

When a rodent goes to a stream to drink, all it needs is to fill its stomach.

2

3

You want to give the world to me, but what would I do with it?

Besides, you've already taken care of everything. Are you trying to give me a good name? What good is empty fame?

Fame is holding an esteemed position, but people often bring suffering upon themselves in striving for it. The only way to reach true reality is to abandon all thought of accomplishment and fame.

4

矣。」

深林，不过一枝；偃鼠饮河，不过满腹。归休乎君，予无所用天下为！庖人虽不治庖，尸祝不越樽俎而代之

许由曰：「子治天下，天下既已治也。而我犹代子，吾将为名乎？名者实之宾也。吾将为宾乎？鹪鹩巢于

也，不亦劳乎！夫子立，而天下治，而我犹尸之，吾自视缺然。请致天下。」

尧让天下于许由，曰：「日月出矣，而爝火不息，其于光也，不亦难乎！时雨降矣，而犹浸灌，其于泽

《庄子◎逍遥游第一》

自然的箫声——庄子说Ⅰ

5

Who's the Master?

Brain · Ear · Mouth · Heart · Hand · Back

Are they all there to serve me?
How can servants be coordinated?

Do they take turns coordinating each other?
Or is there a genuine master that controls them all?

Whether or not we come to know this master will not alter its genuineness one way or the other.

Everyone has their own genuine mind, which is a miniature of the natural Dao. So if you can act in accordance with it, you will never be far from the Dao.

也，固若是芒乎？其我独芒，而人亦有不芒者乎？

功，苶然疲役而不知其所归，可不哀邪！人谓之不死，奚益！其形化，其心与之然，可不谓大哀乎？人之生

一受其成形，不化以待尽。与物相刃相靡，其行进如驰，而莫之能止，不亦悲乎！终身役役而不见其成

相治乎？其递相为君臣乎？其有真君存焉？如求得其情与不得，无益损乎其真。

百骸、九窍、六藏，赅而存焉，吾谁与为亲？汝皆说之乎？其有私焉？如是皆有为臣妾乎？其臣妾不足以

《庄子◎齐物论第二》

Zhuangzi Speaks about Not Speaking

1 A person's body has arms, legs, joints, orifices, and vital organs. How are these all coordinated?

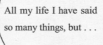
All my life I have said so many things, but . . .

2
I have never really said a single word.

We are always debating one thing or another, but does what we say really mean anything? Maybe it would be better to say nothing and continue merrily on our way.

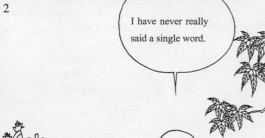
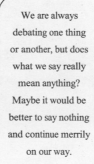

矣，而未知吾所謂之其果有謂乎，其果無謂乎？

者，有未始有無也者，有未始有夫未始有無也者。俄而有無矣，而未知有無之果孰有孰無也。今我則已有謂

雖然，請嘗言之。有始也者，有未始有始也者，有未始有夫未始有始也者。有「有」也者，有「無」也

今且有言于此，不知其與是類乎？其與是不類乎？類與不類，相與為類，則與彼無以異矣。

自然的簫聲　莊子說 I

《莊子◎齊物論第二》

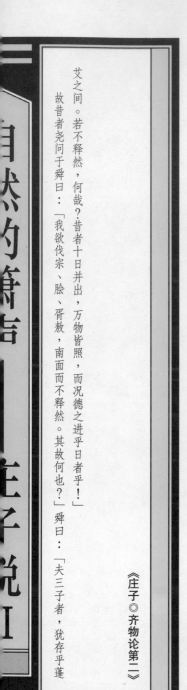

The Danger of Knowledge

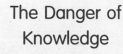

A lifetime is limited, but knowledge is limitless.

1

To take a limited life and pursue limitless knowledge can be very hazardous.

2

3

4

To know it is hazardous and still think that knowledge makes you smarter is even more dangerous.

We should transcend knowledge, rather than be burdened or tied down by it. Knowledge is used in understanding the principles of nurturing life, but once we understand, we should just follow the natural transformations and not pursue superfluous knowledge.

吾生也有涯，而知也无涯。以有涯随无涯，殆已；已而为知者，殆而已矣。为善无近名，为恶无近刑。缘督以为经，可以保身，可以全生，可以养亲，可以尽年。

《庄子◎养生主第三》

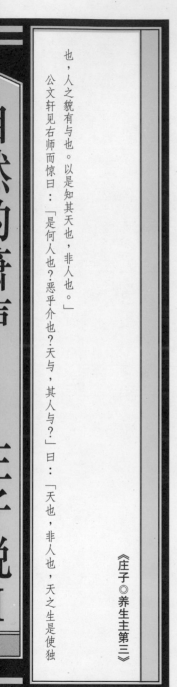

《庄子◎养生主第三》

The Man With One Leg

When Gongwen Xuan first saw an official with only one leg, he was very surprised . . .

1

Then after thinking about it, he finally realized . . .

He may only have one leg, but as long as he was born that way rather than having had it cut off, it is in accordance with nature!

2

If everyone were born with one leg we would think it very unnatural to suddenly see someone with two legs. As long as someone is born the way they are, be it with one leg, two legs, or as many legs as a millipede, it is natural.

We have to live with the body we are born with and deal with circumstances as they come. If we can do this, then we won't feel cold in water or hot in fire, and we will encounter no obstacles in life.

Qin Shi Didn't Cry

After Laozi died, Qin Shi went to pay his respects. He let out a few sniffles and then left.

1

Hey, aren't you a friend of the master's? Is that an appropriate way to pay your respects?

2

A few sniffles is just right.

3

Laozi was born when it was time for him to come into the world, and he died when it was time to leave. If you let things happen and abide in the natural changes, you needn't feel any grief.

4

Upon hearing this, Laozi's disciples stopped their sorrowful crying.

By accepting the transformations of nature, we free ourselves from the bondage of capricious emotions. Qin Shi understood this, and that's why he didn't grieve over Laozi.

5

老聃死，秦失吊之，三号而出。

弟子曰：「非夫子之友邪？」

曰：「然。」

「然则吊焉若此，可乎？」

曰：「然。始也吾以为至人也，而今非也。向吾入而吊焉，有老者哭之，如哭其子；少者哭之，如哭其母。彼其所以会之，必有不蕲言而言，不蕲哭而哭者。是遁天倍情，忘其所受，古者谓之遁天之刑。适来，夫子时也；适去，夫子顺也。安时而处顺，哀乐不能入也，古者谓是帝之悬解。」

《庄子◎养生主第三》

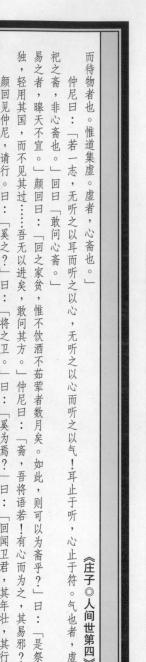

而待物者也。惟道集虚。虚者，心斋也。」

仲尼曰：「若一志，无听之以耳而听之以心，无听之以心而听之以气！耳止于听，心止于符。气也者，虚

祀之斋，非心斋也。」回曰：「敢问心斋。」

易之者，暤天不宜。」颜回曰：「回之家贫，惟不饮酒不茹荤者数月矣。如此，则可以为斋乎？」曰：「是祭

独，轻用其国，而不见其过……吾无以进矣，敢问其方。」仲尼曰：「斋，吾将语若！有心而为之，其易邪？

颜回见仲尼，请行。曰：「奚之？」曰：「将之卫。」曰：「奚为焉？」曰：「回闻卫君，其年壮，其行

《庄子◎人间世第四》

The Man on Fire

A prince of Chu named Zigao was about to depart to the state of Qi as an envoy . . .

1 My mission this time is very serious. If I fail, I will have wronged my sovereign, and if I succeed, I will still be plagued by ill health due to the stress.

2 I will suffer either way. Please tell me what to do.

3 How do you feel right now?

4 I'm so worried I feel like I'm on fire, and I just want to guzzle cold water to put it out.

5 You can stop worrying because in life there are two things that are unavoidable. One is fate, and one is righteousness. The relationship between a parent and a child is one of fate. The relationship between a sovereign and vassal is one of righteousness.

6 So in these two kinds of situations you must set aside thoughts of yourself and thoughts of gain and loss, and just act as the circumstances dictate, that's all.

Don't try to change fate or force success, just follow the natural circumstances and do your best.

自然的箫声　庄子说Ⅰ

《庄子◎人间世第四》

叶公子高将使于齐，问于仲尼曰：「王使诸梁也甚重，齐之待使者，盖将甚敬而不急。匹夫犹未可动，而

况诸侯乎！吾甚栗之。……」

仲尼曰：「天下有大戒二：其一，命也；其一，义也。子之爱亲，命也，不可解于心；臣之事君，义也，

无适而非君也，无所逃于天地之间。是之谓大戒。是以夫事其亲者，不择地而安之，孝之至也；夫事其君者，

不择事而安之，忠之盛也。……为人臣子者，固有所不得已。行事之情而忘其身，何暇至于悦生而恶死！夫子其

行可矣。……」

13

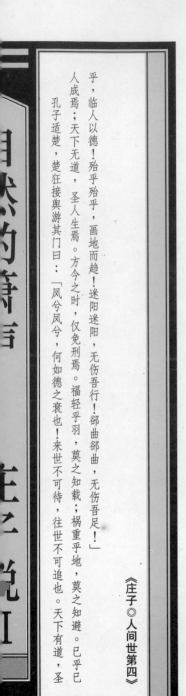

《庄子◎人间世第四》

孔子适楚，楚狂接舆游其门曰：「凤兮凤兮，何如德之衰也！来世不可待，往世不可追也。天下有道，圣

人成焉；天下无道，圣人生焉。方今之时，仅免刑焉。福轻乎羽，莫之知载；祸重乎地，莫之知避。已乎已

乎，临人以德！殆乎殆乎，画地而趋！迷阳迷阳，无伤吾行！郤曲郤曲，无伤吾足！」

The Madman of Chu

Panel 1: When Confucius was traveling to the various states advising sovereigns, he came to the state of Chu. Jieyu, known as the madman of Chu, saw that Confucius was endangering himself through his agenda of virtue and advised him with a song . . .

Panel 2: Oh Phoenix! Oh Phoenix! What can you do in a world of declining virtue! When the Dao is in the land, a sage may succeed, but when the Dao is absent, a sage can only try to survive!

Panel 3: Forget it! Forget it! In these times, don't use your brilliance to show up other people's blemishes.

Panel 4: Oh brambles, oh brambles, you can't hurt my feet, for I walk a crooked path. In choosing whether to go out into the world or retire in reclusion, the wise person will be careful in his timing.

Do People Have Emotions?

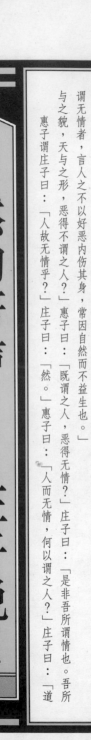

What is a Genuine Person

1 Only a genuine person can have genuine wisdom.

2 The genuine people of old
Were not discouraged by failure,
Were not proud of success,
And did not scheme for things.

3 The did not regret missed opportunities, and when they successfully grasped opportunity, they were not conceited about it.

4 On mountain peaks, they didn't shiver,

5 In water, they didn't feel wet,

6 And in fire they didn't feel hot.

7 Only wisdom such as this can attain to the realm of the Dao.

Dao

Not joyful at birth, not refusing death; gladly accepting things as they happen; not using the intellect to harm the Dao; not contriving to assist nature this is a genuine person!

也，若然者，登高不栗，入水不濡，入火不热。是知之能登假于道者也若此。

且有真人而后有真知。何谓真人？古之真人，不逆寡，不雄成，不谟士。若然者，过而弗悔，当而不自得

《庄子◎大宗师第六》

自然的簫声——庄子说Ⅱ

17

Mindless of Each Other

Hiding the World in the World

Nature changes constantly. Anyone who loves life and hates death doesn't understand the principles of nature.

But of course people fear death!

1

This kind of person is like someone who hides his boat in a mountain,

2

Or his carriage on an island. He thinks it's secure.

3

Then in the middle of the night a giant comes along and carries the whole mountain away. Meanwhile, that person is still lost in his dreams, confident the boat is safely hidden away.

4

Give life and death over to nature. Hiding the world in the world is the proper way to emulate Nature, the great master.

夫藏舟于壑，藏山于泽，谓之固矣。然而夜半有力者负之而走，昧者不知也。藏小大有宜，犹有所遁。若夫藏天下于天下而不得所遁，是恒物之大情也。特犯人之形而犹喜之。若人之形者，万化而未始有极也，其为乐可胜计邪！故圣人将游于物之所不得遁而皆存。善夭善老，善始善终，人犹效之，又况万物之所系，而一化之所待乎！

《庄子◎大宗师第六》

自然为善吾——庄子说I

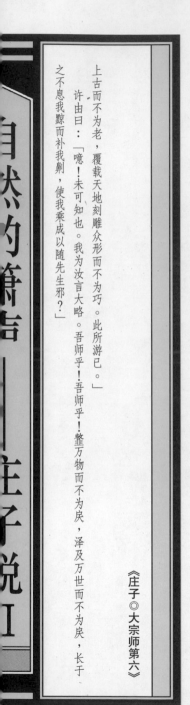

上古而不为老，覆载天地刻雕众形而不为巧。此所游已。」

许由曰：「噫！未可知也。我为汝言大略。吾师乎！吾师乎！鳌万物而不为戾，泽及万世而不为仁，长于

之不息我黥而补我劓，使我乘成以随先生邪？」

《庄子◎大宗师第六》

6 Wuzhuang forgot her pretty face, Juliang forgot his great strength, and the Yellow Emperor forgot his great wisdom—all when they attained the Dao.

7 These were the results of rigorous training! Who knows if nature won't heal my punctures and replace my nose and allow me to follow you?

8 Yes, who knows! So I'll give you a sense of it. Nature is my teacher. When autumn frost freezes the myriad things, it's not an intentional punishment. When spring rains nourish the myriad things, it's not out of benevolence! It carves out the forms of all things, but not to show off its skill.

9 Yierzi, if you want to wander in the natural Dao, follow me.

The transformations of nature happen without intention. The spring rains and autumn frost don't intend to bring life or destruction. Nature's creation and destruction are not really creation and destruction, because there is no net increase or decrease.

自然的箫声——庄子说Ⅱ

「回益矣。」曰：「何谓也？」曰：「回坐忘矣。」仲尼蹴然曰：「何谓坐忘？」颜回曰：「堕肢体，黜聪明，离形去知，同于大通，此谓坐忘。」仲尼曰：「同则无好也，化则无常也，而果其贤乎！丘也请从而后也。」

《庄子◎大宗师第六》

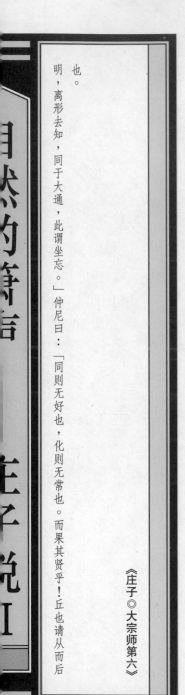

The Mind is Like a Mirror

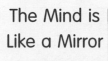

1

Do not pursue fame,
Do not occupy yourself with scheming,
Do not concern yourself with trifles,
Do not strive for great wisdom.

2

Experience the boundless and wander in infinity. Use what heaven has given you without boasting about achievements. Just be empty.

The perfect person's mind is like a mirror, accepting things as they come and go, neither welcoming them in, nor showing them out.

3

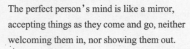

And he responds to things naturally without storing them up. Therefore, he is able to overcome material things and not be harmed by them . . .

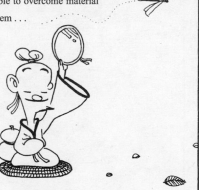

The perfect person treats the mind like a mirror. When something happens, he responds, and when its over, he empties his mind of it. He genuinely appreciates every moment of life.

4

自然的箫声　庄子说 I

已。至人之用心若镜，不将不迎，应而不藏，故能胜物而不伤。

无为名尸，无为谋府；无为事任，无为知主。体尽无穷，而游无朕；尽其所受乎天，而无见得，亦虚而

《庄子◎应帝王第七》

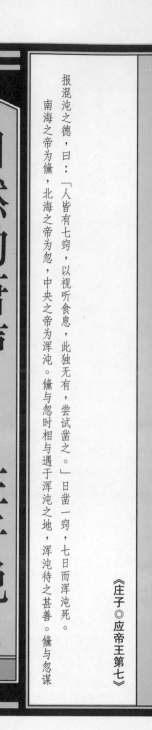

《庄子◎应帝王第七》

报混沌之德，曰：「人皆有七窍，以视听食息，此独无有，尝试凿之。」日凿一窍，七日而混沌死。

南海之帝为儵，北海之帝为忽，中央之帝为浑沌。儵与忽时相与遇于浑沌之地，浑沌待之甚善。儵与忽谋

自然为萧言　庄子说Ⅰ

The Death of Primal Chaos

1

The name of the emperor of the North Sea was Suddenly.

The name of the emperor of the South Sea was Hastily.

The name of the Central emperor was Primal Chaos.

2

Hastily and Suddenly often went to the land of Primal Chaos, and Primal Chaos treated them with great generosity.

3

Everyone has seven orifices to see, hear, eat, and breath with. Why don't we make some for Primal Chaos as a little gift.

Good idea!

4

So Hastily and Suddenly made some orifices for Primal Chaos . . .

5

One per day . . .

6

And on the seventh day, Primal Chaos passed away.

Non-action is the essence of nature. If it is tampered with by the ingenuity of petty intelligence, it will break down and end up passing away.

Wine

The Sixth Finger

Some people are born with the big toe fused to the next toe.

1

And some people are born with six fingers on one hand.

2

These are not of any special use, but as long as they are born that way, it is natural.

3

Having an extra finger is really neat. I want six fingers, too.

4

5

You're asking too much.

Instituting benevolence and righteousness are likc asking for a useless birth defect. Some people may have them naturally, but to actively pursue them is being greedy, and greed is not in accord with nature.

之行，而多方于聪明之用也。

而非道德之正也。是故骈于足者，连无用之肉也；枝于手者，树无用之指也；骈枝于五藏之情者，淫僻于仁义之行，而多方于聪明之用也。

骈拇枝指，出乎性哉！而侈于德。附赘县疣，出乎形哉！则侈于性。多方乎仁义而用之者，列于五藏哉！

《庄子◎应帝王第八》

27

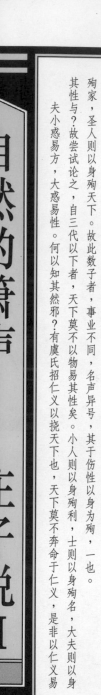

The Horse Trainer's Transgressions

A horse's hooves can stand on frost and snow, and its fur can protect it from cold winds.

1

It eats grass and drinks water, then stretching it's legs it leaps into the air. This is the original nature of horses.

2

If you were to build a luxurious mansion for it, the horse would see it as useless.

3

But ever since the great horse trainer Bo Le, the situation has changed . . .

I'm best at training horses!

4

之，渴之，驰之，骤之，整之，齐之，前有橛饰之患，而后有鞭笑之威，而马之死者已过半矣。陶者曰：「我善至伯乐，曰：「我善治马。」烧之，剔之，刻之，雒之，连之以羁馽，编之以皂栈，马之死者十二三矣；饥马，蹄可以践霜雪，毛可以御风寒，龁草饮水，翘足而陆，此马之真性也。虽有义台路寝，无所用之。及

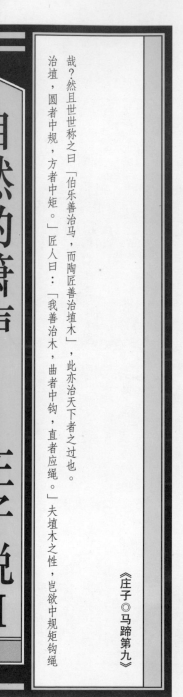

5. They use hot metal to make the coats glisten, clip the manes, trim the hooves, and brand them.

6. Treated this way, two or three out of ten horses die.

7. Then they train them for endurance, disciplining them through hunger and thirst.

8. They use a whip to control the speed, alternating between fast and slow . . .

9. After these tortures and being shut up in a stable and losing their freedom, half of all horses will die.

Through non-intentional action, the people are naturally transformed. Through tranquillity and non-interference, the people are naturally upright. A sage tries to govern by contriving propriety, music, righteousness, and benevolence, and with them, hypocrisy and deceit arise.

The Harm of Benevolence and Righteousness

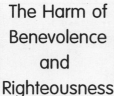

1 In highest antiquity, people lived contentedly, oblivious to what they were doing or where they were going.

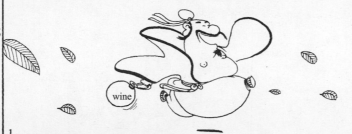

wine

2 Completely at ease, they walked around with protruding bellies and wandered where they would.

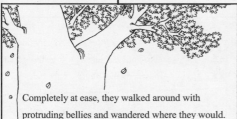

wine

3 Then sages came along contriving propriety and music to rectify people's appearances and postulating benevolence and righteousness to transform their original natures.

wine

4 From then on, people began boasting of themselves, deceiving others, and contending for advantages, all in an unstoppable wave.

With the destruction of the Dao, benevolence and righteousness arise. With the coming of intelligence, deception and hypocrisy arise. In highest antiquity, people were ignorant yet honest. They didn't even know what deception and hypocrisy were, so why would they need benevolence and righteousness?

wine

自然的箫声——庄子说Ⅰ

《庄子◎马蹄第九》

匡天下之形，县跂仁义以慰天下之心，而民乃始踶跂好知，争归于利，不可止也。此亦圣人之过也。

夫赫胥氏之时，民居不知所为，行不知所之，含哺而熙，鼓腹而游，民能以此矣。及至圣人，屈折礼乐以

31

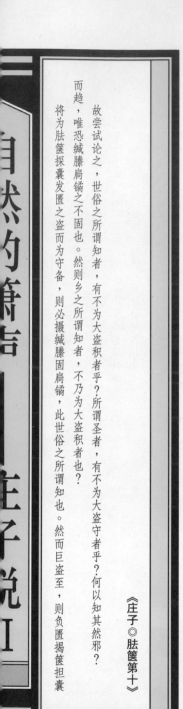

自然的箴言　庄子说 I

故尝试论之，世俗之所谓知者，有不为大盗积者乎？所谓圣者，有不为大盗守者乎？何以知其然邪？而趋，唯恐缄縢扃鐍之不固也。然则乡之所谓知者，不乃为大盗积者也？将为胠箧探囊发匮之盗而为守备，则必摄缄縢固扃鐍，此世俗之所谓知也。然而巨盗至，则负匮揭箧担囊

《庄子◎胠箧第十》

The Lost Pearl

1 One day, the Yellow Emperor traveled north of the Chi river and ascended a slope of the Kunlun mountains.

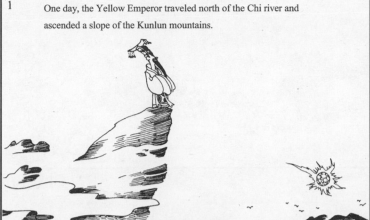

2 On his way back, he lost his mysterious pearl . . .

3 He ordered Knowledge to go look for it, but he couldn't find it.

4 Then he sent Li Zhu to look for it with his keen eyes, but he couldn't find it.

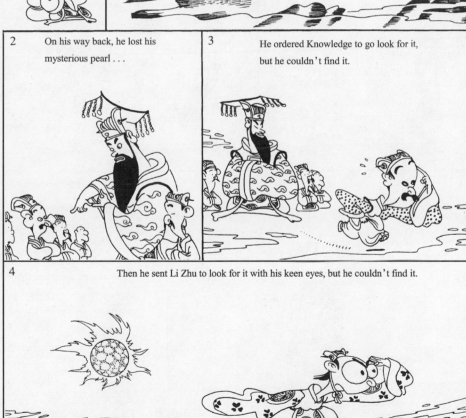

黄帝游乎赤水之北，登乎昆仑之丘而南望，还归遗其玄珠。使知索之而不得，使离朱索之而不得，使吃诟索之而不得也。

乃使象罔，象罔得之。黄帝曰：「异哉！象罔乃可以得之乎？」

《庄子◎天地第十二》

5 Chi Gou, the great debater, searched, but he couldn't find it either.

6 Formless, why don't you go look for it.

Yes, your majesty.

7 Finally, it was Formless who found the mysterious pearl.

Here it is, your majesty.

8 How strange that only Formless was able to find the pearl!

The Dao cannot be obtained by way of the knowledge, the senses, or debate. Only non-intention and non-affectation can find it— because the Dao is a realm beyond the intellect and the senses.

The Heavenly Dao

1. The heavenly Dao courses without end, and thus the myriad things arise.

2. The imperial Dao courses without end, and thus the entire land pays allegiance.

3. The sagely Dao courses without end, and thus all within the four seas pay homage.

Dao

The coursing of the Dao is unending, and in the natural realm the myriad things move about of their own accord. The sage emulates the Dao and looks after the myriad things with a serene mind.

万物之镜也。夫虚静恬淡寂漠无为者，天地之本，而道德之至，故帝王圣人休焉。心者，故静也。水静则明烛须眉，平中准，大匠取法焉。天地之鉴也，圣，六通四辟于帝王之德者，其自为也，昧然无不静者矣。圣人之静也，非曰静也善，故静也；万物无足以铙天道运而无所积，故万物成；帝道运而无所积，故天下归，圣道运而无所积，故海内服。明于天，通于

心，非曰静也善，水静犹明，而况精神，圣人之心静乎！

《庄子◎天道第十三》

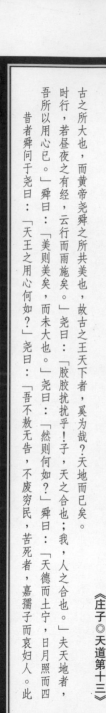

《庄子◎天道第十三》

Governing Through Non-Action

Independent Leisure

1

Curbing ambition and praising conduct, seeing oneself as special and separate from the world, sermonizing and bemoaning the evils of the world—these are but for the sake of something higher and are what forest hermits, cynics, and idealists like to do.

2

Speaking of benevolence, righteousness, conscientiousness, and trustworthiness, respecting frugality, and promoting humility—these are but for the sake of self-cultivation and are what political hopefuls, instructors, and itinerant scholars like to do.

3

Speaking of great accomplishments, establishing great reputations, maintaining the sovereign-vassal relationship, and rectifying the superior-inferior relationships— these are but for the sake of governing and are what court patrons, citizens of superpowers, and aggressors like to do.

之人，彭祖寿考者之所好也。

此江海之士，避世之人，间暇者之所好也。吹呴呼吸，吐故纳新，能经鸟申，为寿而已矣；此导引之士，养形为治而已矣；此朝廷之人，尊主强国之人，致功并兼者之所好也。就薮泽，处闲旷，钓鱼闲处，无为而已矣；此平世之士，教诲之人，游居学者之所好也。语大功，立大名，礼君臣，正上下，为治而已矣；此平世之士，教诲之人，游居学者之所好也。语大功，立大名，礼君臣，正上下，为治而已矣；

信，恭俭推让为修而已矣；此平世之士，教诲之人，游居学者之所好也。语大功，立大名，礼君臣，正上下，

刻意尚行，离世异俗，高论怨诽，为亢而已矣；此山谷之士，非世之人，枯槁赴渊者之所好也。语仁义忠

自然的箫声 庄子说 L

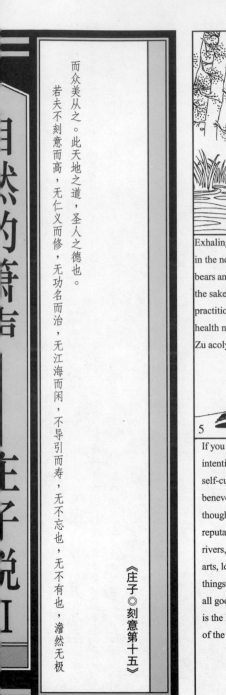

而众美从之。此天地之道，圣人之德也。

若夫不刻意而高，无仁义而修，无功名而治，无江海而闲，不导引而寿，无不忘也，无不有也，澹然无极

《庄子◎刻意第十五》

Energy and Spirit

1
If the body toils without rest, it will become fatigued . . .

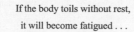

2
If one's energy is used without a break, it will be exhausted . . .

3
For instance, it is the nature of water to be pure when it is not made turbid, to be calm when it is not stirred up . . .

4
If it is blocked up and unable to flow, it cannot be pure. This is a natural phenomenon.

5
So it is said that purity without turbidity, tranquillity without alteration, simplicity without action, movement with the natural way are all the Dao of nurturing the spirit.

6
The spirit is like a precious sword. It should be kept in a case and not imprudently removed.

Common people emphasize profit, upright people emphasize reputation, worthies praise ambition, and sages cherish the spirit!

同帝。

之，不轻敢用也，宝之至也。精神四达并流，无所不极，上际于天，下蟠于地，化育万物，不可为象，其名为之象也。故曰，纯粹而不杂，静一而不变，惔而无为，动而天行，此养神之道也。夫有干越之剑者，柙而藏之，不轻敢用也。故曰，形劳而不休则弊，精用而不已则竭。水之性，不杂则清，莫动则平；郁闭而不流，亦不能清；天德之象也。

《庄子◎刻意第十五》

39

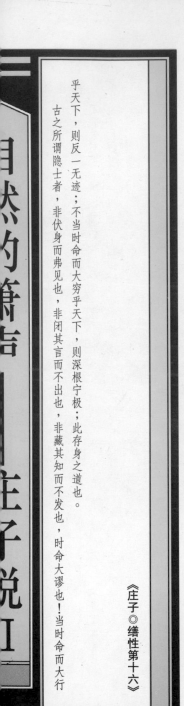

平天下，則反一无迹；不当时命而大穷乎天下，则深根宁极；此存身之道也。

古之所谓隐士者，非伏身而弗见也，非闭其言而不出也，非藏其知而不发也，时命大谬也！当时命而大行

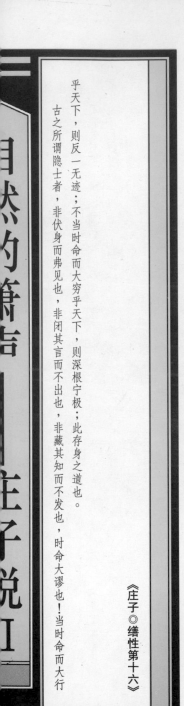

《庄子◎缮性第十六》

Recluses

Recluses of old didn't necessarily hide themselves away from the world.

1

They were men of great wisdom, and at the appropriate times they would come out to implement the Dao throughout the land . . .

2

If the times were not appropriate,   they would conceal their wisdom, become one with nature, and disappear from sight.

3

In the past, people who knew how to take care of themselves did not go around pointing out their own wisdom; they didn't use their timing and ingenuity to bring suffering to the people; and they didn't let greed tie down their own virtue.

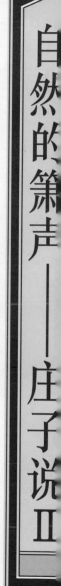

自然的箫声——庄子说 Ⅱ

北海若曰：「井龜不可以語于海者，拘于虛也；夏蟲不可以語于冰者，篤于時也；曲士不可以語于道者，

束于教也，吾非至于子之門，則殆矣，吾長見笑于大方之家。」

「聞道百以為莫己若者」，我之謂也。且夫我嘗聞少仲尼之聞而輕伯夷之義者，始吾弗信；今我睹子之難窮

順流而東行，至于北海，東面而視，不見水端，于是焉河伯始旋其面目，望洋向若而嘆曰：「野語有之曰：

秋水時至，百川灌河，涇流之大，兩涘渚崖之間不辯牛馬。于是焉河伯欣然自喜，以天下之美為盡在己。

41

似尔向之自多于水乎？」

所运，三王之所争，仁人之所忧，任士之所劳，尽此矣。伯夷辞之以为名，仲尼语之以为博，此其自多也，不

人处一焉；人卒九州，谷食之所生，舟车之所通，人处一焉；此其比万物也，不似豪末之在于马体乎？五帝之

何时止于不盈；尾闾泄之，不知何时已而不虚……计中国之在海内，不似稊米之在大仓乎？号物之数谓之万，

束于教也。今尔出于崖涘，观于大海，乃知尔丑，尔将可与语大理矣。天下之水，莫大于海，万川归之，不知

《庄子◎秋水第十七》

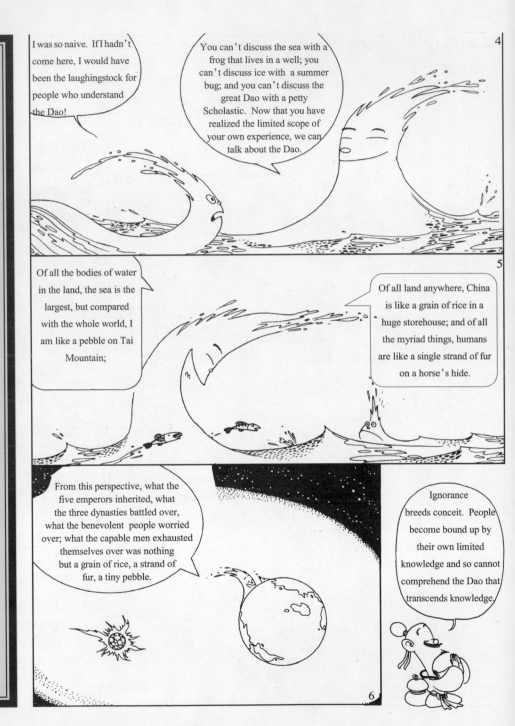

Heaven and Earth and a Strand of Fur

自然的箫声——庄子说Ⅱ

《庄子◎秋水第十七》

河伯曰：「然则吾大天地而小（毫）末，可乎？」

北海若曰：「否，夫物，量无穷，时无止，分无常，终始无故。是故大知观于远近，故小而不寡，大而不

多，知量无穷，证曏今故，故遥而不闷，掇而不跂；察乎盈虚，故得而不喜，失而不忧，知分之无

常也；明乎坦涂，故生而不说，死而不祸，知终始之不可故也。……由此观之，又何（毫）以知末之足以定至

细之倪，又何以知天地之足以穷至大之域！

43

自然的箫声——庄子说Ⅰ

河伯曰：「世之议者皆曰：『至精无形，至大不可围。』是信情乎？」

北海若曰：「夫自细视大者不尽，自大视细者不明。故异便，此势之有也。夫精，小之微也；垺，大之殷

也；夫精粗者，期于有形者也；无形者，数之所不能分也；不可围者，数之所不能穷也。可以言论者，物之粗

也；可以意致者，物之精也；言之所不能论，意之所不能致者，不期精粗焉。」

《庄子◎秋水第十七》

Size and Limits

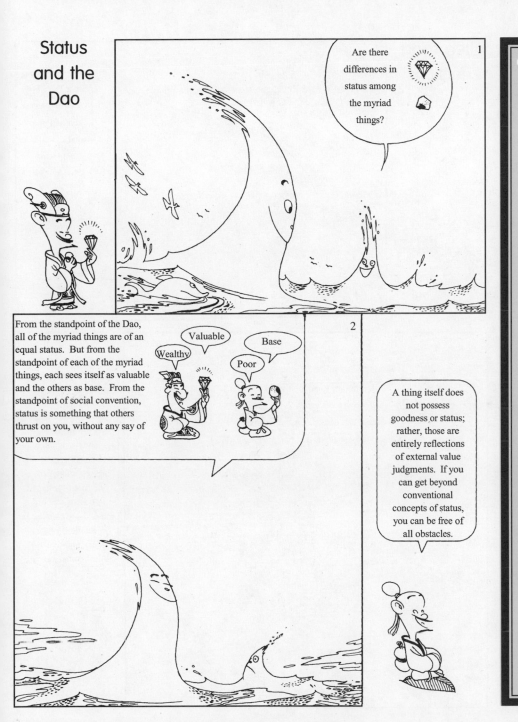

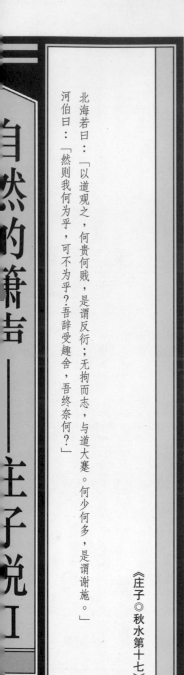

Alternating Functions

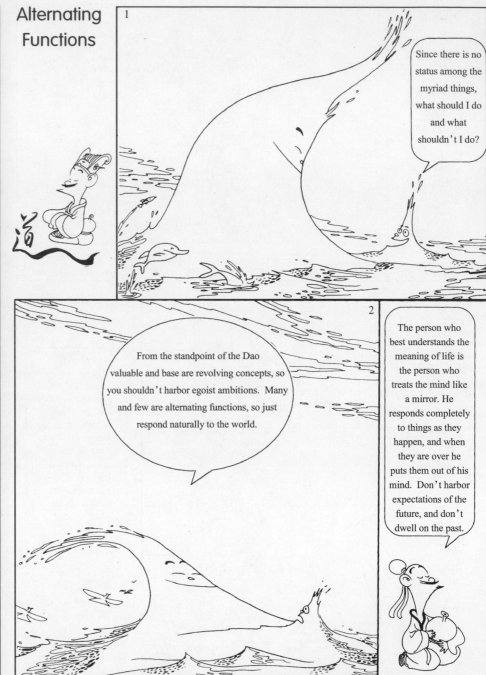

Fire Doesn't Burn

内，人在外，德在乎天。知乎人之行，本乎天，位乎得；蹢躅而屈伸，反要而语极。」

溺，寒暑弗能害，禽兽弗能贼。非谓其薄之也，言察乎安危，宁于祸福，谨于去就，莫之能害也。故曰，天在

北海若曰：「知道者必达于理，达于理者必明于权，明于权者不以物害己。至德者，火弗能热，水弗能

河伯曰：「然则何贵于道邪？」

《庄子◎秋水第十七》

47

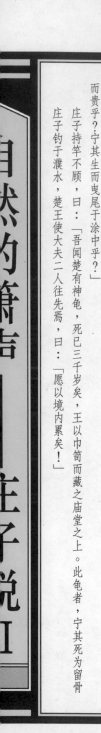

庄子钓于濮水，楚王使大夫二人往先焉，曰：「愿以境内累矣！」

庄子持竿不顾，曰：「吾闻楚有神龟，死已三千岁矣，王以巾笥而藏之庙堂之上。此龟者，宁其死为留骨

而贵乎？宁其生而曳尾于涂中乎？」

二大夫曰：「宁生而曳尾于涂中。」

庄子曰：「往矣！吾将曳尾于涂中。」

《庄子◎秋水第十七》

自然的箫声　庄子说 I

49

《庄子◎至乐第十八》

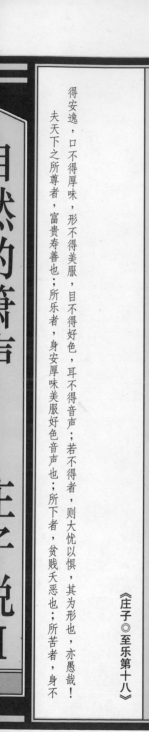

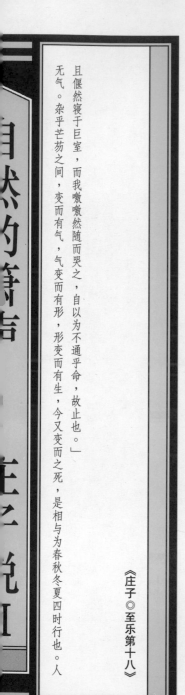

《庄子◎至乐第十八》

且偃然寝于巨室，而我嗷嗷然随而哭之，自以为不通乎命，故止也。」

无气。杂乎芒芴之间，变而有气，气变而有形，形变而有生，今又变而之死，是相与为春秋冬夏四时行也。人

子列子问关尹曰：「至人潜行不窒，蹈火不热，行乎万物之上而不栗。请问何以至于此？」

关尹曰：「是纯气之守也，非知巧果敢之列。居，予语汝！凡有貌象声色者，皆物也，物与物何以相远？夫奚足以至乎先？是形色而已。则物之造乎不形而止乎无所化，夫得是而穷之者，物焉得而止焉！彼将处乎不淫之度，而藏乎无端之纪，游乎万物之所终始，壹其性，养其气，合其德，以通乎物之所造。夫若是者，其天守全，其神无却，物奚自入焉！」

《庄子◎达生第十九》

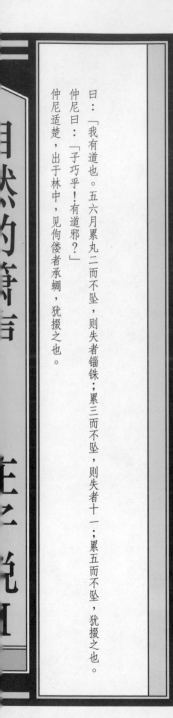

Catching
Cicadas

Then I put three balls on the tip of my pole, and if they don't fall off, my chances of missing a cicada are one in ten;

Then I do five balls, and if they don't fall off, I can catch the cicadas as if I were using my bare hand.

When I catch cicadas, my body is as still as a tree trunk, and the pole in my hand is as steady as a branch . .

And despite the expansiveness of the world and the multitude of things in it, all I see are the cicada wings, and nothing else can distract me from them. So how can I miss?

Students, pay attention! An undistracted mind brings concentration of the spirit.

For an expert archer, there is no bow or arrow, no self or other; attention is concentrated on the target and the self coalesces with the surroundings; the myriad appearances enter the mind, but the mind takes no heed.

孔子顾谓弟子曰：「用志不分，乃凝于神，其佝偻丈人之谓乎！」

物易蜩之翼，何为而不得！」

吾处身也，若橛株枸；吾执臂也，若槁木之枝；虽天地之大，万物之多，而唯蜩翼之知。吾不反不侧，不以万

《庄子◎达生第十九》

自然的箫声——庄子说Ⅱ

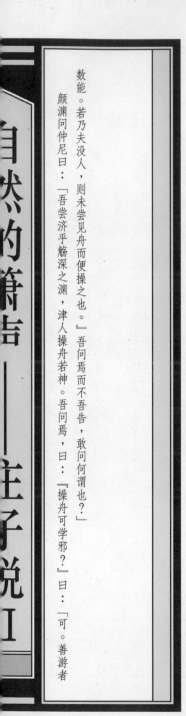

颜渊问仲尼曰：「吾尝济乎觞深之渊，津人操舟若神。吾问焉，曰：『操舟可学邪？』曰：「可。善游者数能。若乃夫没人，则未尝见舟而便操之也。」吾问焉而不吾告，敢问何谓也？」

Steering a Boat

Yan Hui asked Confucius:

1 Once when I was crossing the Shangshen Depths, I noticed the ferryman steering his boat with supernatural ease.

2 Can steering a boat be learned?

Sure. If you know how to swim, you can learn very fast.

3 If you skin dive, you'll know how to do it even if you've never seen a boat before.

4 I asked him more, but he didn't answer. What did he mean?

A swimmer can learn fast because he is at ease in water.

5 A skin diver knows how to steer a boat without even having seen one before because to him the depths are like hills and a boat capsizing is no worse than a carriage tipping over.

6 Since the thought of capsizing wouldn't bother him, he would be able to steer with ease and confidence!

If betting inexpensive tiles, an archer would shoot well and without the least reservation.

If betting precious belt-hooks, he would feel a little unsettled and his accuracy would reflect it. And if betting gold, the burden would be too much and would lose all accuracy.

7

A good swimmer forgets the water and so can come and go with ease. If your mind becomes attached to something external you will lose your concentration and your skill. That's why it's said that "the ordinary mind is the Dao".

The skill-level of the archer doesn't change, but as soon as he begins to care, he is paying attention to something external; and whenever you pay attention to something external, you lose your internal composure.

8

自然的箫声——庄子说I

所矜，则重外也。凡外重者内拙。

也。覆却万方陈乎前而不得入其舍，恶往而不暇！以瓦注者巧，以钩注者惮，以黄金注者殙。其巧一也，而有

仲尼曰：「善游者数能，忘水也。若乃夫没人之未尝见舟而便操之也，彼视渊若陵，视舟之覆犹其车却

《庄子◎达生第十九》

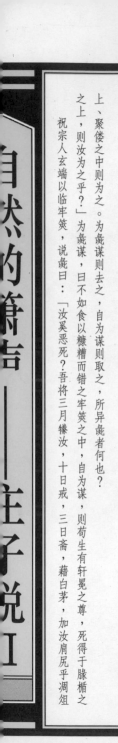

自然的箫吉——主子兑Ⅱ

其由是与！
消；然后入山林，观天性；形躯至矣，然后成见锯，然后加手焉；不然则已。则以天合天，器之所以疑神者，

怀庆赏爵禄，斋五日，不敢怀非誉巧拙；斋七日，辄然忘吾有四枝形体也。当是时也，无公朝，其巧专而外滑

对曰：「臣工人，何术之有！虽然，有一焉。臣将为锯，未尝敢以耗气也，必斋以静心。斋三日，而不敢

梓庆削木为锯，锯成，见者惊犹鬼神。鲁侯见而问焉，曰：「子何术以为焉？」

《庄子◎达生第十九》

Dongye Ji Has an Accident

1 Dongye Ji was a famous carriage driver, and one time when he was working with Duke Zhuang's horses, he ran the horses a hundred times around the track.

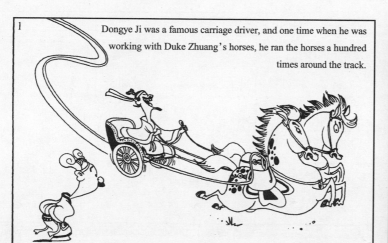

2 Yan He saw this and went to the Duke:

Something's going to happen to Dongye's horses.

Really?

3

Dongye Ji just had an accident.

How did you know something would happen?

The horses' energy was already expended, and he was still pushing them. So I knew something had to happen.

Overzealousness can unsuspectingly exhaust your energy, and the result can be disastrous.

4

自然的箫声——庄子说Ⅱ

东野稷以御见庄公，进退中绳，左右旋中规。庄公以为文弗过也，使人钩百而反。

颜阖遇之，入见曰：「稷之马将败。」公密而不应。

少焉，果败而反。公曰：「子何以知之？」

曰：「其马力竭矣。而犹求焉，故曰败。」

《庄子◎达生第十九》

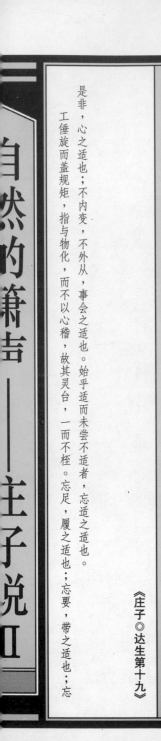

《庄子◎达生第十九》

自然的箫声——主子说 II

是非，心之适也；不内变，不外从，事会之适也。始乎适而未尝不适者，忘适之适也。

工倕旋而盖规矩，指与物化，而不以心稽，故其灵台，一而不桎。忘足，履之适也；忘要，带之适也；忘

Zhuangzi in the Brambles

Panel 1: Wearing ragged clothes and straw sandals, Zhuangzi had an audience with the king of Wei.

How come you suffer such hardship, Zhuangzi?

Panel 2: This is poverty, not hardship! Hardship is when one has high ideals but can't realize them.

Panel 3: When a monkey is in tall trees, it jumps around and swings from vine to branch with great ease. It's so at home that even the great archer Hou Yi couldn't get it.

eep eep

Panel 4: But when it is among brambles, the monkey is very cautious and doesn't dare make any rash movement . . .

Panel 5: Right now I am living in a dark time and feel like I am among brambles.

In life there will be good times and bad. If you live in a violently chaotic world, it may be best to quietly accept poverty, because if you don't, you may end up like Bi Gan, who tried to realize his ideals under a brutal despot and had his heart cut out for it.

自然的箫声——庄子访口

庄子衣大布而补之，正纆系履而过魏王。魏王曰：「何先生之惫邪？」庄子曰：「贫也，非惫也。士有道

德不能行，惫也；衣弊履穿，贫也，非惫也；此所谓非遭时也。王独不见夫腾猿乎？其得枏梓豫章也，揽蔓其

枝而王长其间，虽羿、蓬蒙不能眄睨也。及其得柘棘枳枸之间也，危行侧视，振动悼栗；此筋骨非有加急而不

柔也，处势不便，未足以逞其能也。今处昏上乱相之间，而欲无惫，奚可得邪？此比干之见剖心，徵也夫！」

《庄子◎山木第二十》

必为其服也∵为其服者∵未必知其道也。公固以为不然，何不号于国中曰∵「无此道而为此服者，其罪死？」

庄子曰∵「周闻之，儒者冠圜冠者，知天时∵履句屦者，知地形∵缓佩玦者，事至而断。君子有其道者，未

哀公曰∵「举鲁国而儒服，何谓少乎？」

庄子曰∵「鲁少儒。」

庄子见鲁哀公。哀公曰∵「鲁多儒士，少为先生方者。」

Only One Confucian in Lu

When Zhuangzi had an audience with Duke Ai of Lu, the Duke said:

Here in Lu, everyone is a Confucian, no one practices Daoism!

Actually, there are very few Confucians in Lu!

1

2

3

Haven't you seen everyone in Confucian clothes? How can you say there aren't many?

4

I have heard that the round cap of the Confucian represents his knowledge of astronomy, his rectangular shoes represent his knowledge of geography, and his jade belt ornaments represent his decisiveness.

Astronomy

Decisiveness

Geography

A gentleman of good cultivation doesn't necessarily need to wear this kind of costume, and a man who wears this kind of costume isn't necessarily a gentleman of good cultivation.

5

I request that you make an edict, saying that all those who aren't well-versed in Confucianism and yet wear Confucian-style clothes be put to death. Then we'll see how many real Confucians there are.

O.K.!

6

庄子曰：「以鲁国而儒者一人耳，可谓多乎？」

于是哀公号之五日，而鲁国无敢儒服者，独有一丈夫儒服而立乎公门。公即召而问以国事，千转万变而不贫。

《庄子◎田子方第二十一》

67

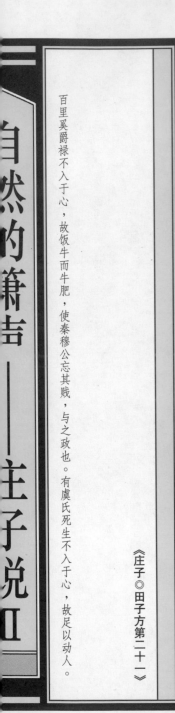

自然的箴言——主子兑Ⅱ

百里奚爵禄不入于心，故饭牛而牛肥，使秦穆公忘其贱，与之政也。有虞氏死生不入于心，故足以动人。

《庄子◎田子方第二十一》

Baili Xi Raises Oxen

When Baili Xi worked raising oxen, he didn't dwell on it being a lowly job, so they turned out big and plump.   1

Qin's Duke Mu was impressed by Baili Xi's being able to disregard his lowliness and so gave him a government position and a noble title.   2

As a nobleman, Baili Xi didn't dwell on his prestigious status, so his administration was very successful.   3

If you can disregard your status, you will become selfless. If in doing government work, you don't dwell on status, seek wealth, or aim for great achievements, how can you fail?

The Genuine Painter

1 Once when Duke Yuan of Song wanted a painting done, he called together various painters to choose the best one. One by one they stood up, bowed respectfully, then moved to one side readying brush and ink.

2 There was one painter who showed up late and had a certain unconstrained air about him,

3 And when he was ordered to stand up and bow, he refused and left.

4 The Duke sent someone to investigate:

He takes off his clothes and sits cross-legged on the floor. I can't believe it!

5 Perfect. This is the painter I was looking for!

A genuine person doesn't dwell on status or pay. A painter must be genuine before he can produce "genuine" works of art.

自然的箫声——庄子说Ⅱ

宋元君将画图，众史皆至，受揖而立；舐笔和墨，在外者半。有一史后至者，儃儃然不趋，受揖不立，因之舍。公使人视之，则解衣般礴臝。君曰：「可矣，是真画者也。」

《庄子◎田子方第二十一》

69

于是无人遂登高山，履危石，临百仞之渊，背逡巡，足二分垂在外，揖御寇而进之。御寇伏地，汗流至踵。

伯昏无人曰：「是射之射，非不射之射也。尝与汝登高山，履危石，临百仞之渊，若能射乎？」

列御寇为伯昏无人射，引之盈贯，措杯水其肘上，发之，适矢复沓，方矢复寓。当是时，犹象人也。

Perfect Archery

Liezi demonstrated his archery for Bohun Wuren. He set a cup of water on his arm, and fired arrow after arrow with alarming speed.

1

2 When the first arrow had been released, the next arrow was already in the bow; yet he was as still as a stake and not a drop of water spilled out of the cup.

3 Your archery is good, but it is still intentional. You've yet to attain an unintentional skill.

4 Come with me!

Self-Respect

自然的箫声——主子兑 II

肩吾问于孙叔敖说：「子三为令尹而不荣华，三去之而无忧色。吾始也疑子，今视子之鼻间栩栩然，子之用心独奈何？」

孙叔敖曰：「吾何以过人哉！吾以其来不可却也，其去不可止也，吾以为得失之非我也，而无忧色而已矣。我何以过人哉！且不知其在彼乎，其在我乎？其在彼邪？亡乎我；在我邪？亡乎彼。方将踌躇，方将四顾，何暇至乎人贵人贱哉！」

《庄子◎田子方第二十一》

1 — Jian Wu asked Sunshu Ao: You have been prime minister three times without feeling especially prestigious, and you have been demoted three times without feeling especially anxious. How are you able to do this?

2 — When wealth and prestige come, I can't push them away; and when they go, I can't stop them from going. Since I can't control gain and loss, what is there to be anxious about?

3 — What's more, I don't know if the prestige lies in being prime minister or in myself. If it's in being prime minister, then it has nothing to do with me, and if it's in me, then it has nothing to do with being prime minister.

4 — I take pride in myself, so what do I care about conventional views of status!

For the perfect person, a wise person cannot preach to him, a beautiful person cannot seduce him, a bandit cannot rob him, and matters of life and death cannot move him—let alone such insignificant things as status or pay!

《庄子◎知北游第二十二》

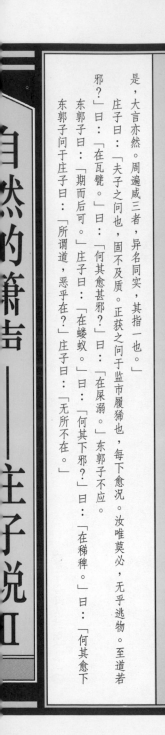

自然的箫声——庄子说Ⅱ

东郭子问于庄子曰：「所谓道，恶乎在？」庄子曰：「无所不在。」东郭子曰：「期而后可。」庄子曰：「在蝼蚁。」曰：「何其下邪？」曰：「在稊稗。」曰：「何其愈下邪？」曰：「在瓦甓。」曰：「何其愈甚邪？」曰：「在屎溺。」东郭子不应。庄子曰：「夫子之问也，固不及质。正获之问于监市履狶也，每下愈况。汝唯莫必，无乎逃物。至道若是，大言亦然。周遍咸三者，异名同实，其指一也。」

盈虚，彼为衰杀非衰杀，彼为本末非本末，彼为积散非积散也。

其所穷。物物者与物无际，而物有际者，所谓物际者也；不际之际，际之不际者也。谓盈虚衰杀，彼为盈虚非

吾志，无往焉而不知其所至，去而来而不知其所止，吾已往来焉而不知其所终；彷徨乎冯闳，大知入焉而不知

尝相与游乎无何有之宫，同合而论，无所终穷乎，尝相与无为乎！澹而静乎！漠而清乎！调而闲乎！寥已

《庄子◎知北游第二十二》

75

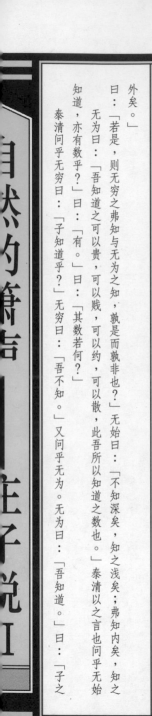

应应之，是无内也。以无内待问穷。若是者，外不观乎宇宙，内不知乎大初，是以不过乎昆仑，不游乎太虚。」

无始曰：「有问道而应之者，不知道也。虽问道者，亦未闻道。道无问，问无应。无问问之，是问穷也；无

应应之，是无内也。

名。」

无始曰：「道不可闻，闻而非也；道不可见，见而非也；道不可言，言而非也。知形形之不形乎！道不当

于是泰清中而叹曰：「弗知乃知乎！知乃不知乎！孰知不知之知？」

《庄子◎知北游第二十二》

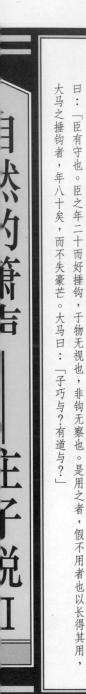

而況乎无不用者乎！物孰不資焉！」

曰：「臣有守也。臣之年二十而好捶鉤，于物无視也，非鉤无察也。是用之者，假不用者也以長得其用，

大馬之捶鉤者，年八十矣，而不失豪芒。大馬曰：「子巧與？有道與？」

《莊子◎知北游第二十二》

Breaking the Barriers

1 A student studies what he can't study.

2 A do-er does what he can't do.

3 A debater debates what he can't debate.

4 A knowledge-seeker set his sights on what he can't know.

5 If this weren't the case, natural equanimity would be lost.

The nature of nature is constant change. If you do the same things or study the same things over and over, how are you different from a corpse?

自然的箫声——庄子说Ⅱ

有不即是者，天钧败之。

学者，学其所不能学也；行者，行其所不能行也；辩者，辩其所不能辩也。知止乎其所不能知，至矣；若

《庄子◎庚桑楚第二十三》

亲，至信辟金。

蹍市人之足，则辞以放骜，兄则以妪，大亲则已矣。故曰，至礼有不人，至义不物，至知不谋，至仁无

【庄子◎庚桑楚第二十三】

Ultimate Benevolence

1

Ow!

Ooops, I'm sorry! Please excuse me!

If you step on a stranger's foot, you must apologize and show remorse.

If you step on your older brother's foot, you must comfort him a bit.

Ooops, are you O.K.?

Ow!

2

If you step on your father's foot, you don't have to do anything.

Love is not having to say you're sorry!

Ow!

3

Ultimate propriety is to not distinguish between self and other; ultimate righteousness is to not distinguish between self and things; ultimate wisdom is to not scheme; ultimate benevolence is to not distinguish between remote and intimate; ultimate trust does not seek valuables as collateral.

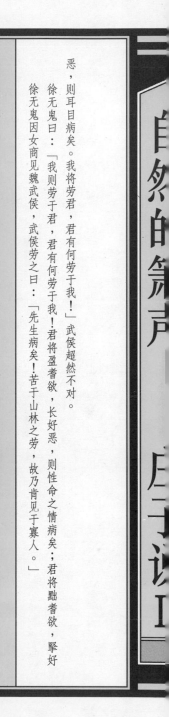

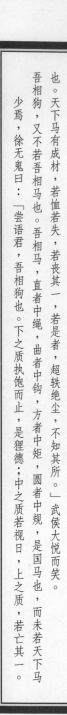

《庄子◎徐无鬼第二十四》

少焉，徐无鬼曰：「尝语君，吾相狗也。下之质执饱而止，是狸德；中之质若视日，上之质，若亡其一。

也。天下马有成材，若恤若失，若丧其一，若是者，超轶绝尘，不知其所。」武侯大悦而笑。

吾相狗，又不若吾相马也。吾相马，直者中绳，曲者中钩，方者中矩，圆者中规，是国马也，而未若天下马

A medium-grade dog has bright eyes and acts superior to others.

6

A high-grade dog is so calm and composed, it forgets it's even a dog! 7

Ha ha ha, well-said, well-said.

I'm even better at appraising horses. There are two kinds of horses: the state horse and the universal horse.

What's a state horse?

8

Regardless of its teeth or back or head or eyes, if a horse obeys the bridle and reins and acts completely within the confines of its training, it is a state horse. 9

What's a universal horse, then? 10

A universal horse has an innate character. It is so serene that it seems to forget its own body. And when this kind of horse runs, it nearly flies. That's what a universal horse is.

Wonderful, wonderful! You know your horses, all right!

11

曰：「子不闻夫越之流人乎？去国数日，见其所知而喜；去国旬月，见所尝见于国中者喜；及期年也，见似

女商曰：「若是乎？」
徐无鬼曰：「吾直告之吾相狗马耳。」

弢，奉事而大有功者不可为数，而吾君未尝启齿。今先生何以说吾君，使吾君说若此乎？」

徐无鬼出，女商曰：「先生独何以说吾君乎？吾所以说吾君者，横说之则以诗书礼乐，从说之则以金板六

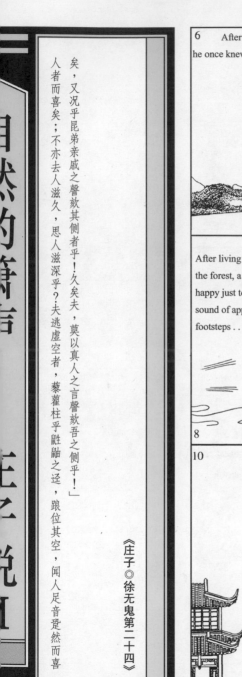

《庄子◎徐无鬼第二十四》

The King Kills a Special Monkey

1. Once when the king of Wu went into the mountains to hunt monkeys, all the monkeys ran away deeper into the mountains, except one. That monkey stayed up in the tree, jumping and swinging around, not the least bit afraid of people.

eep eep

2. Nyah, nyah. Can't get me!

3. Everybody open fire.

We're not leaving till we get it.

4. !

5. This monkey was special, but showing off got it killed.

Don't boast about your talents and intelligence. A revealing glint can bring harm, so it's best to obscure you brilliance.

自然的箫声 庄子说

哉！」颜不疑归而师董梧以锄其色，去乐辞显，三年而国人称之。

王顾谓其友颜不疑曰：「之狙也，伐其巧，恃其便以敖予，以至此殛也！戒之哉！嗟乎，无以汝色骄人

敏给搏捷矢。王命相者趋射之，狙执死。

吴王浮于江，登乎狙之山。众狙见之，恂然弃而走，逃于深蓁，有一狙焉，委蛇攫搔，见巧乎王。王射之，

《庄子◎徐无鬼第二十四》

85

自然勺箫信 庄子说Ⅰ

《庄子◎徐无鬼第二十四》

尽有天，循有照，冥有枢，始有彼。则其解之也似不解之者，其知之也似不知之也，不知而后知之。

缘之，大方体之，大信稽之，大定持之。

知大一，知大阴，知大目，知大均，知大方，知大信，知大定，至矣。大一通之，大阴解之，大目视之，大均

故足之于地也践，虽践，恃其所不蹍而后善博也；人之于知也少，虽少，恃其所不知而后知天之所谓也。

The Realm of Ignorance

1. Your foot only needs a piece of ground the size of your shoe, but to go any distance, you also depend on the ground that the feet don't walk on.

2. We don't know much, and yet it is by relying on that which we don't know that we can come to understand nature.

3. Perfection is: realizing the grand unity, the grand mystery, the grand vision, the grand equanimity, the grand magnanimity, the grand trust, and the grand serenity.

4. To realize the grand unity is to understand the Dao,
To realize the grand mystery is to unravel the mystery of the Dao,
To realize the grand vision is to see the Dao,
To realize the grand equanimity is to flow with the Dao,
To realize the grand magnanimity is to experience the Dao,
To realize the grand trust is find the truth in the Dao,
To realize the grand serenity is to maintain the Dao.

5. We should all follow nature, be in accordance with the myriad things, conceal the Daoist mind, and understand ourselves and others.

In this kind of realm, resolving the mystery of the Dao is like the time before it was resolved, and realizing the Dao is like the time before it was realized—knowledge comes only after recognizing our ignorance.

The Cyclic Dao

The great sage Ran Xiang realized the significance of the cycle and how it is a sequential composition of unceasing transformations.

For the myriad things, there is no past, no present, no future.

1

2

The body becomes one with the myriad things, and the genuine self doesn't leave even for a moment. Nature is emulated, but not intentionally. There isn't even an idea of nature or of people.

The Dao is without beginning or end, without a motive force, and without time. To be in accord with it, we follow the myriad things on their cyclic path, forever changing and forever tranquil.

3

所行之备而不洫，其合之也若之何？

师天，与物皆殉，其以为事也若之何？夫圣人未始有天，未始有人，未始有始，未始有物，与世偕行而不替，

冉相氏得其环中以随成，与物无终无始，无几无时。日与物化者，一不化者也，阖尝舍之！大师天而不得

《庄子◎则阳第二十五》

自然的箫声

庄子说I

任公子为大钩巨缁，五十犗以为饵，蹲乎会稽，投竿东海，旦旦而钓，期年不得鱼。已而大鱼食之，牵巨钩，锱没而下，骛扬而奋鬐，白波若山，海水震荡，声侔鬼神，惮赫千里。任公子得若鱼，离而腊之，自制河以东，苍梧已北，莫不厌若鱼者。已而后世辁才讽说之徒，皆惊而相告也。夫揭竿累，趋灌渎，守鲵鲋，其于得大鱼难矣。饰小说以干县令，其于大达亦远矣。是以未尝闻任氏之风俗，其不可与经于世亦远矣。

《庄子◎外物第二十六》

The Prince of Ren Goes Fishing

1. A prince of Ren once made a huge hook and a giant pole, used fifty steers as bait, crouched down on Kuaiji Mountain, tossed his line into the Eastern Sea, and fished for a big fish.

2. After waiting patiently for a whole year, he got a bite, and it was an enormous fish that created waves as high as mountains.

whoosh!

3. The prince drew up the fish, had it chopped into pieces, and it was enough to feed all the people for miles around.

4. People who like legends, love the prince of Ren story and always run off to tell others about it.

I'm telling you, that fish was huge!

5. As for those who fish for small fish with small poles, they don't believe any of it.

Nonsense!

Petty scholastics will never understand the great Dao! They go on their tiny bit of limited knowledge and experience, and deny the great Dao that is beyond knowledge.

Confucius Changes

Panel 1: Confucius lived for sixty years, and he changed for sixty years.

Panel 2: What he had thought was wrong in the past he might have thought to be right in the present. What he thought to be right in the present, he might have thought was wrong in the past.

Panel 3: Huizi asked Zhuangzi:

Did Confucius work hard to fulfill his ambitions and put his knowledge to use.

Confucius was beyond that.

Panel 4: He felt that although debating right and wrong could win verbal assent, it couldn't win people's hearts. If you want to win people's hearts, you must act in accordance with the natural Dao.

Putting intelligence to use is a lesser stratum. A wise person goes beyond this stratum.

自然的箫声——庄子说 II

庄子谓惠子曰：「孔子行年六十而六十化，始时所是，卒而非之，未知今之所谓是之非五十九非也。」

惠子曰：「孔子勤志服知也。」

庄子曰：「孔子谢之矣，而其未之尝言。孔子云：『夫受才乎大本，复灵以生。鸣而当律，言而当法，利义陈乎前，而好恶是非直服人之口而已矣。使人乃以心服，而不敢蘁立，定天下之定。』已乎已乎！吾且不得及彼乎！」

89

自然的箫声——主子说 II

曰：「既已县矣。夫无所县者，可以有哀乎？彼视三釜三千钟，如观鸟雀蚊虻相过乎前也。」

弟子问于仲尼曰：「若参者，可谓无所县其罪乎？」

曾子再仕而心再化，曰：「吾及亲仕，三釜而心乐；后仕，三千钟而不洎亲，吾心悲。」

《庄子◎寓言第二十七》

No Attachments

1. The second time Zengzi worked as an official, he experienced a change of attitude . . .

Before when I was an official, my salary was only five pecks of grain, and yet I was very happy—because my parents were alive then.

2. Now my salary is fifteen thousand bushels and I feel just terrible.

3. Master, can a person like Zengzi be considered to have no attachments?

4. He isn't attached to his salary, but he does have attachments. Does a person with no attachments feel happiness or sadness?

5. A person with no attachments views a salary of five pecks or fifteen thousand bushels as he would a sparrow or a mosquito passing by.

Zengzi may not have been attached to his salary, but he had certainly been attached to his parents, and this is why he felt sad. Anyone who has feelings of happiness or sadness has attachments.

The Phases of Attaining the Dao

Yancheng Ziyou said to Dongguo Ziqi:

The first year I studied with you, I was like a wild horse.

1

The second year, I began to settle down a little,

2

The third year, my mind had no obstacles.

3

The fourth year, I became one with the external world.

4

5

The fifth year, all things turned toward me.

The sixth year, I understood the spiritual world.

The seventh year, I flowed with nature.

The eighth year, I dispensed with thoughts of life and death.

The ninth year, I attained profound enlightenment.

When cultivating the Dao, don't over-emphasize self-control. By following your own self-nature, you will gradually be able to forget the self and finally attain profound enlightenment. If you try for too much self-control the very first year, you'll still be a wild horse in ten years.

自然的箫声——庄子说Ⅱ

颜成子游谓东郭子綦曰：「自吾闻子之言，一年而野，二年而从，三年而通，四年而物，五年而来，六年

而鬼入，七年而天成，八年而不知死，不知生，九年而大妙。」

《庄子◎寓言第二十七》

91

Life Is Most Important

自然的箫吉——王子兑 II

天下也。
忧之病，方且治之，未暇治天下也。」夫天下至重也，而不以害其生，又况他物乎！唯无以天下为者，可以托
尧以天下让许由，许由不受。又让于子州支父，子州支父曰：「以我为天子，犹之可也。虽然，我适有幽

《庄子◎让王第二十八》

1 Yao wished to abdicate and hand the world over the Xu You, but Xu You wouldn't accept . . .

So Yao tried Zizhou Zhifu . . .

I would accept . . .

2

But I have a very worrisome illness. Because I've got to get that cured, I'm afraid I won't have time to govern the land.

3

Emperor is the most powerful position in the world, but there are some who would refuse to exchange their lives for it. This is what separates a person of the Dao from a common person.

92

The Goat Butcher Refuses Reward

1 When King Zhao of Chu fled the country, Yue the goat butcher fled with him. After the Wu army retreated and King Zhao returned . . .

The king would like to reward those who endured hardships with him. You are one.

Goat Meat

2

3 When the king fled, I also abandoned my business. Now he has returned, and I am butchering goats again, so what's to be rewarded?

4 You went through a lot with the king, and he'd like you to accept a small token of his appreciation.

5 I didn't cause him to flee or return, so I don't think I should be punished or rewarded.

Society's praising and blaming are usually just mutual deception. If you can see through this, you will be without any obstacles whatever, and your mind will be pure and carefree.

93

位而不怍。」丘诵之久矣，今于回而后见之，是丘之得也。」

孔子愀然变容曰：「善哉回之意！丘闻之，『知足者不以利自累也，审自得者失之而不惧，行修于内者无

所学夫子之道者足以自乐也。回不愿仕。」

颜回对曰：「不愿仕。回有郭外之田五十亩，足以给饘粥；郭内之田十亩，足以为丝麻；鼓琴足以自娱，

孔子谓颜回曰：「回，来！家贫居卑，胡不仕乎？」

《庄子◎让王第二十八》

Refusing Office

Confucius said to Yan Hui:

Hui, your family is so poor and your home is so run-down, why don't you be an official?

But master, I don't want to be an official!

2

I have eighteen acres of poor fields outside the city wall, and the meager harvest is enough rice gruel for me to live on.

3

Inside the wall, I have half an acre and that's enough to provide me with clothes and shoes.

4

In my spare time, I play the zither or study the Dao under you. I'm perfectly happy like this, so why should I be an official?

Don't pursue a superfluous amount of material things, otherwise, you will become a slave to them. People who are contented and easily amused won't put themselves out for the sake of profit.

The Man Who Pursued Profit

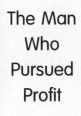

fame fortune

1 Cao Shang of Song was sent as emissary to Qin. The Qin king liked him very much and so bestowed him with one hundred carriages.

2 I'm not any good at living in run-down alleys, weaving sandals for a living, or going hungry. My specialty is cajoling a hundred carriages from a ten-thousand carriage sovereign.

3 When the king gets an illness that needs cured, he gives a carriage away to the person who can cure him . . .

4 To the person who licks his boils, he gives five carriages. The more demeaning the task, the greater the number of carriages.

5 What despicable thing did you do to get so many carriages?

People often go against their own nature and do demeaning and despicable things in pursuit of profit and status. A gentleman is easygoing and high-minded. There are things he will do, and there are things he won't do.

自然的箫声——庄子说 II

宋人有曹商者，为宋王使秦。其往也，得车数乘；王说之，益车百乘。反于宋，见庄子曰：「夫处穷闾阨巷，困窘织屦，槁项黄馘者，商之所短也；一悟万乘之主而从车百乘者，商之所长也。」

庄子曰：「秦王有病召医，破痈溃痤者得车一乘，舐痔者得车五乘，所治愈下，得车愈多。子岂治其痔邪，何得车之多也？子行矣！」

《庄子◎列御寇第三十二》

图字：01－2005－0835

图书在版编目（CIP）数据

庄子说Ⅱ＝Zhuangzi Speaks Ⅱ：More Music of Nature/蔡
志忠绘．—北京：现代出版社，2005
ISBN 7-80188-515-5

Ⅰ．庄…　Ⅱ．蔡…　Ⅲ．漫画-作品集-中国-现代　Ⅳ．J228.2

中国版本图书馆 CIP 数据核字（2005）第 025583 号

Zhuangzi Speaks Ⅱ：More Music of Nature
庄子说Ⅱ：自然的箫声

作者/〔台湾〕蔡志忠
译者/〔美〕Brian Bruya
总策划/吴江江
责任编辑/张　璐
封面设计/刘　刚
出版发行/现代出版社（北京安外安华里 504 号　邮编：100011）
印刷/中国电影出版社印刷厂
开本/880×1230　1/24　4 印张
版次/2005 年 5 月第 1 版
　　　2005 年 6 月第 2 次印刷
印数/6001～9000 册
书号/ISBN 7-80188-515-5
定价/9.80 元